Fire Escape

The Dead Man Files

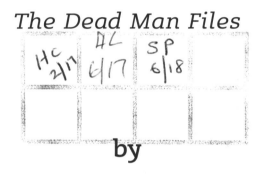

by

Alan Combes

Illustrated by Stephen Elford

First published in 2009 in Great Britain by
Barrington Stoke Ltd
18 Walker St, Edinburgh, EH3 7LP

www.barringtonstoke.co.uk

Title ISBN: 978-1-84299-703-1
Pack ISBN: 978-84299-788-8

Printed in Great Britain by The Charlesworth Group

Dead Man File

Name: Luke Smith

Age: 16

Cause of death: Car crash. Serious head and back injuries.

Date of case 4: September 2009

Mission: To help my friend before it's too late ...

Contents

Intro

Luke Smith was killed in a car driven by his best mate, Joe. But that was not the end of it. Luke comes back as a ghost. What can he do to help people now he is dead?

Name:
Luke Smith
Age:
16

Chapter 1

One of my best places before I died was the rec. My mates Dan and Jonny used to meet me there. They were brothers and we all had great fun.

They missed me after I was killed in the
crash.

That year in November at the rec, the gang made a giant bon-fire. I saw it get bigger and bigger as it got nearer to Bon-fire Night, but no one saw me.

Name:
Luke Smith
Age:
16

Chapter 2

The Red Skulls, a gang from town, had been our enemies for a long time.

Their boss, Matt Gibb, saw Dan out on his own one day at the rec. Five of the Red Skulls jumped him.

They tied him up and kept him in a shed
for days.

"What's going on?" Dan asked.

"Wait and see, punk," Matt Gibb told
him.

Name:
Luke Smith
Age:
16

Chapter 3

So Dan was now a missing person. The cops were out looking for him. No luck! I saw where he was, but what could I do?

The Red Skulls had an evil plan.

Name:
Luke Smith
Age:
I6

Chapter 4

"The night before November 5th, we tie him up and gag him," said Matt Gibb to the other Red Skulls. "Then we hide him in the middle of the bonfire."

"He'll fry alive," one Red Skull said.

"Bad luck," Matt Gibb said. "We won't be the ones torching the bon-fire."

Name:
Luke Smith
Age:
I6

Chapter 5

On November 5th, Dan's brother, Jonny, was just about to torch the bon-fire. He would kill his brother Dan and never know.

Suddenly I had an idea. I used my
powers to phone Dan from Jonny's mobile.
I could hear Dan's mobile ringing in the
middle of the unlit bon-fire.

"It's coming from over there," Jonny said, pointing to the bon-fire.

Dan's ring tones were loud and clear.

Chapter 6

"He's in the middle of the bon-fire," Jonny said. "Shift everything."

The gang freed Dan. Dan told Jonny, "I don't get it. My mobile rang, but it was turned off."

"That is so weird," Jonny said.

Only I knew the answer.

Like this book? Why not try the next one coming soon?

Secret Santa

Luke Smith is dead. But he's back to help those who need it.

There's a killer on the loose and Luke's brother's in trouble ... has Luke met his match?

For more info check out our website:
www.barringtonstoke.co.uk

Also coming soon ...

The Look-out

Luke Smith is dead. But he's back to help those who need it.

Two men plan to rob Luke's gran and will stop at nothing to get what they want ... Can Luke save her?

For more info check out our website:
www.barringtonstoke.co.uk